CATOONS FROM CATLAND

Books by Vernon Coleman include:

The Medicine Men (1975)
Paper Doctors (1976)
Stress Control (1978)
The Home Pharmacy (1980)
Aspirin or Ambulance (1980)
Face Values (1981)
The Good Medicine Guide (1982)
Bodypower (1983)
Thomas Winsden's Cricketing Almanack (1983)
Diary of a Cricket Lover (1984)
Bodysense (1984)
Life Without Tranquillisers (1985)
The Story Of Medicine (1985, 1998)
Mindpower (1986)
Addicts and Addictions (1986)
Dr Vernon Coleman's Guide To Alternative Medicine (1988)
Stress Management Techniques (1988)
Know Yourself (1988)
The Health Scandal (1988)
The 20 Minute Health Check (1989)
Sex For Everyone (1989)
Mind Over Body (1989)
Eat Green Lose Weight (1990)
How To Overcome Toxic Stress (1990)
Why Animal Experiments Must Stop (1991)
The Drugs Myth (1992)
Complete Guide To Sex (1993)
How to Conquer Backache (1993)
How to Conquer Pain (1993)
Betrayal of Trust (1994)
Know Your Drugs (1994, 1997)
Food for Thought (1994, revised edition 2000)
The Traditional Home Doctor (1994)
People Watching (1995)
Relief from IBS (1995)
The Parent's Handbook (1995)
Men in Dresses (1996)
Power over Cancer (1996)

The OFPIS File (2008)
Cat Tales (2008)
What Happens Next? (2009)
Moneypower (2009)
Bloodless Revolution (2009)

novels
The Village Cricket Tour (1990)
The Bilbury Chronicles (1992)
Bilbury Grange (1993)
Mrs Caldicot's Cabbage War (1993)
Bilbury Revels (1994)
Deadline (1994)
The Man Who Inherited a Golf Course (1995)
Bilbury Pie (1995)
Bilbury Country (1996)
Second Innings (1999)
Around the Wicket (2000)
It's Never Too Late (2001)
Paris In My Springtime (2002)
Mrs Caldicot's Knickerbocker Glory (2003)
Too Many Clubs And Not Enough Balls (2005)
Tunnel (1980, 2005)
Mr Henry Mulligan (2007)
Bilbury Village (2008)
Bilbury Pudding (2009)

as Edward Vernon
Practice Makes Perfect (1977)
Practise What You Preach (1978)
Getting Into Practice (1979)
Aphrodisiacs – An Owner's Manual (1983)

with Alice
Alice's Diary (1989)
Alice's Adventures (1992)

with Donna Antoinette Coleman
How To Conquer Health Problems Between Ages 50 and 120 (2003)
Health Secrets Doctors Share With Their Families (2005)
Animal Miscellany (2008)

CATOONS FROM CATLAND

A Catanalian Carnival
of Catacious Catoons

Vernon Coleman

Chilton Designs

Published by Chilton Designs, Publishing House, Trinity Place,
Barnstaple, Devon EX32 9HG, England.

First published by Chilton Designs in 2009

ISBN: 978 1 898146 08 7

A catalogue record for this book is available from
the British Library.

Printed by CPI Antony Rowe, Chippenham, Wiltshire

Dedication

To Donna Antoinette, cuter and more loveable than any kitten.
My love all ways and always.

Preface

Cats are the most intelligent, most beautiful and most spiritual creatures on the planet. I know this to be true because many cats have told me it is so. Butterflies may be more exotic and their lives, although short, may be more dramatic and carefree but who would choose the life of a butterfly over that of a cat? Rhinoceroses may be more powerful, more imposing and (for want of a better word) more operatic than any other creatures, but I would much rather be a pampered cat than a rampaging rhinoceros. Cats are the most complete creatures and, therefore, the most perfect living beings any of us will ever get to know. Who among us has not secretly envied their lifestyle? Who has believed for a second that a cat would ever envy us?

Of course, cats have their foibles and, whisper it softly, their oh-so-very-little weaknesses. They hate being embarrassed, for example, and we've all seen the way a cat will pretend to be doing something else when it has been caught red-pawed doing something it shouldn't have done. Cats do this, by the way, because they are clever enough to know that if they pretend that something didn't happen, we are so weak and so adoring that we will eventually question our own memories and our judgement and come to believe that what we saw with our own eyes didn't really happen at all. And even if that doesn't work they know that we will be so amused by their little tricks that we will quickly forgive and forget.

'The cat's just broken my priceless Ming vase!'

'Oh, don't fuss so dear. Just look at the sweet way she is licking her bottom and pretending she had nothing to do with it!'

Those of us who know cats always learn a great deal from them.

11

Here's a list of seven things I've learned from cats:

1. Never admit to anything. Move quickly to put as much distance as possible between you and whatever it is for which you are disclaiming responsibility. The message to share is a simple one: 'You weren't there'. Go fast enough and people will wonder if it really happened. Never look back.

2. If in doubt about whether you've got away with it, lick your bottom. If you're licking your bottom people will either be amused or they will feel embarrassed and look away. No one argues with someone who is licking their bottom.

3. Never eat food you don't like. You won't go hungry for long. Someone will always produce food you do like.

4. If you want to find out if a piece of pottery is valuable, try knocking it from a mantelpiece. A valuable vase will always smash. A cheap vase will always bounce.

5. A dog in a locked car is no threat.

6. When you get to the top of the tree, the only thing left is to work out a dignified way to come down.

7. The mouse under the fridge can stay where it is longer than you can stay where you are.

I've no doubt that I will learn a great deal more as the years go by.

The drawings in this book were triggered by several observations. For example, the obvious truth that while many people treat their cats like children others treat them like honoured guests. And then there is the, perhaps less obvious, observation that although many Uprights regard their cats anthropomorphically, the vast majority of cats are undoubtedly guilty of doing whatever the mirror image of anthropomorphism is in their dealings with Uprights.

Finally, I would like to make it clear that nowhere in this book is the reader encouraged to laugh at cats. Sensitive Uprights never laugh at cats or, indeed, even with cats.

If cats are perceived to have a weakness (and I mention this with some trepidation since it is not and never would be my intention to upset the cats among my readers) it is surely the fact that, generally speaking, they are often regarded, even by the most committed ailurophiles, as not having much of a sense of humour. This, of course, is a nonsense for, in the way that the English have a much more sophisticated sense of humour than other nationalities (think, for a moment, of the sort of comedy films produced by the Americans or the Germans), so cats have a much more sophisticated sense of humour than even the English. Cats are never amused by slapstick comedy. They are, however, quietly amused by the absurdities of life as exhibited by Uprights. And so I feel confident that cats will allow us to laugh *for* them as we momentarily share their frustration, embarrassment and amusement at living in a world where Uprights pretend to be in charge, and often genuinely believe that they are.

Vernon Coleman, Catland, March 2009

She: "I think Charlie is anorexic."
He: "He just ate half a rabbit and a mouse!"

"Don't forget! Be back by 11 pm at the latest."

"I had it permed when you said you were taking me out for a night on the tiles."

"I said I'd go on a head," said Tiger.

"Elsie says we've just got five.
But I'm sure we've got more than that."

"How do you know, until you've tasted it?"

"I have to finish the story.
I always tell him a story before we go to bed."

*"There's <u>nothing</u> wrong with the way she purrs.
She's French and she purrs in French."*

"You treat this place like a cattery."

"The Internet is great. They all think I'm a lion."

*"You can't go out to play until you've eaten
all your browns and greys."*

"Mine still needs a little more training, but she's coming on quite nicely. How is yours doing?"

*"You wait all day for a mouse,
and then two come along at once."*

"It's amazing how often people get to look like their owners."

When Fred had a bad fur day, it was a BAD fur day.

A cat on a lap is worth two up a tree.

"My cat doesn't understand me."

31

After eating two mice, a kipper and a bowl of rice pudding,
Pickles felt a little bloated.

Upright: "It's Salmon."
Cat: "No, it isn't. It's liver and tuna from the 'past its sell by
date bin' at the supermarket."

Lady Belinda didn't know much about music,
but she knew what she liked.

*"Do you think he knows the old lady left him
everything in her will?"*

"Why is it sophisticated and sporting when they do it and primitive instinct when we do it?"

"People said it wouldn't last.
But what do they know?"

"They say I'm stuck in my ways so, just to show them, I spent this morning in the airing cupboard and this afternoon in front of the stove. I've never done it <u>that</u> way round before."

39

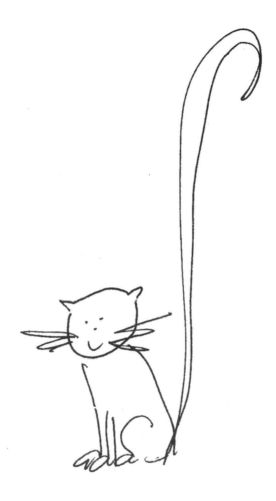

Tiddlelina's tail was so long, she had to curl the tip over to stop it being singed by the sun.

"Yours is much easier to catch than mine."

Safe!

Catisfaction

Tiddles liked nothing better than to curl up on a good book.

"Maybe she's not cut out to be vegetarian."

Just good friends.

"OK. I get the hint."

*"It opens next Thursday.
Would you like to come and see it with me?"*

*"He's the one who'll be using it most,
so he might as well try it out."*

Snowflake admired her new friend.
She thought she was the most beautiful cat she'd ever seen.

"I never catch anything. It's almost as though they seem to know I'm coming. It's spooky."

"Just work your way in from the outside."

Love

"Are you sure you wouldn't find the rug more comfortable?
It's closer to the fire."

*"They said I fell out of the window. I didn't, of course.
I wasn't even there. I was licking my bottom."*

"So, who else around here is in the habit of jumping up onto the mantelpiece?"

"My husband is a cat burglar."

Catnap

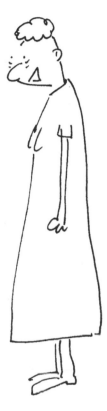

*"If you don't come back here immediately I'll ring my solicitor
and have you taken out of my will."*

The Caterer

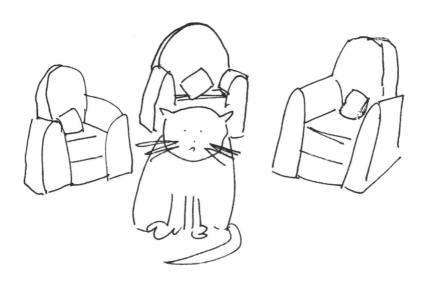

"Choices, choices!" murmured Fluffy to herself.
"Why can't life be simple?"

"I wish I were an Upright," said Tiddles.
"They have such an easy life."

"You should have seen the one that got away."

"Wait for the old one. The young one isn't very good. He gives everyone steroids and has cold hands."

"Why don't you ever sleep on the <u>dirty</u> washing?"

"My Upright is bigger than yours."

*"Her Uprights have been invited to a garden party
at Buckingham Palace."*

69

*"I'm worried about her;
she doesn't seem quite frivolous enough."*

"I'm pretty sure it's one of mine."

"It wasn't difficult to find two matching cats but it took a long time to persuade them to sit still on the mantelpiece."

Jeffrey: "*I think we should hold out for twice as much salmon tomorrow. This is very boring.*"

Marco: "How are you getting on with your new Uprights?"
Jeremy: "Very well. I should have them trained in another
month."

*"I sometimes worry that she doesn't like this brand but eats it and
pretends to like it so that we don't feel guilty."*

"We have to buy that one – it's 7p more expensive than any of the others and she always knows if we don't buy the most expensive one."

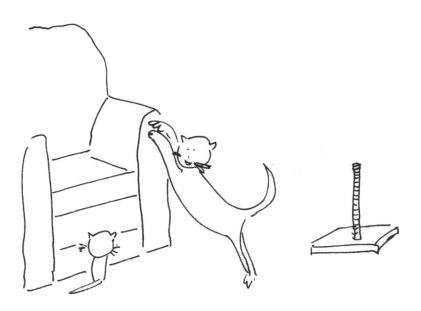

"*Never, ever scratch the post they put out. That's a terribly common thing to do. And, when you scratch, r-e-a-c-h out and really put your back into it.*"

"I'm sorry, I know you're fond of him, but he's really not good enough for you. He comes from a very rough family."

A cat is just a smile-making machine made of fur.

"I'm going to have to take that off you.
Mice aren't good for pregnant cats."

"I'm not going anywhere with you dressed like that!"

*"Sometimes, when I look up at the clouds,
I think I see one that looks like a mouse"*

Dottie was obsessed with cats and loved her cat-shaped suitcase,
though it didn't hold very much and was not very practical.

"Tiddles has never bitten anyone before.
Did you annoy him?"

"I'm sorry, really sorry. I was wrong. Please forgive me.
I promise I won't do it again – whatever it was."

Fluffy: "*I wonder what they think all day.*"
Honey: "*Do they think? Like us, I mean.*"

"I love the little ones.
They're really cute."

"I sometimes think that all they do is sleep all day."

Sarah: *"Is there a God?"*
Mimi: *"No."*
Sarah: *"How can you be so sure?"*
Mimi: *"Because if there was one He'd live in the airing cupboard and I've looked and He's not there."*

"Who says it's good for me?"

I purr, therefore I am.

"I'm going to be a small game hunter when I grow up."

"No, I've never seen her awake, either."

"Why can't the cat have a basket?"

"Why do they always prefer to play with the box it came in?"
"Why don't we just buy the box next time?"

"Do you think they understand what we're saying?"

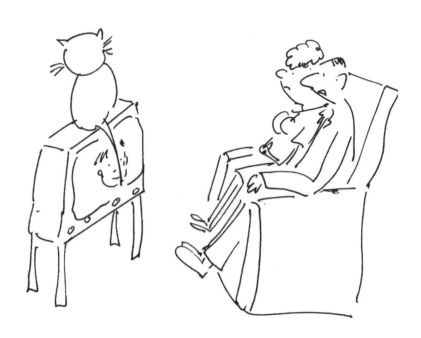

"I suppose one of us had better feed her."

"It was your idea to put the cat out at night."

"Give him a red pill every two hours and a blue pill once every four hours."

"We've just got one big one.
We find it's easier to keep track."

"He likes someone to hold it open for him."

"You spoil that cat!"

"She'll be a heart breaker in two or three days time."

*"Psst...pass it on... there's a mouse-swapping party tonight,
behind the dustbins at No 57."*

*"And you're really sure that's why they put the gap
in the back of the chair?"*

*"He's been really snooty and full of himself ever since he heard you
say that he was descended from an Egyptian cat-god."*

"I'm writing a book about people."

"I don't understand cats. What do they want?"

"I've just come from Mrs Crump's. Her cat has had kittens and she says we can have one or two if we like."

"Whose is that?"

Hyacinth: "I got into a scrap with three Alsatians and a
Rotweiler. What happened to you?"
Chloe: "I fell out of a 47th storey window."

"Mrs Brentwood's cat loves this brand.
And she won a rosette last year."

"Go on! Off you go then. See if I care."

Five minutes later ....
"Tiddles! Where are you, Tiddles? Come here sweetheart. I've got fresh cream for you. Tiddles!"

The End

On the following pages you can find
details of other cat books by
Vernon Coleman.
These may be ordered direct from
our offices in Devon:
Publishing House, Trinity Place,
Barnstaple, Devon EX32 9HG, England

(when ordering please make cheques or postal orders payable to
Publishing House – and add £1 per book towards UK P&P /
£2 per book outside the UK)

or you can visit our web site to order
using a credit or debit card:
www.vernoncoleman.com

ALICE'S DIARY

£9.99 Hardback

Are you looking for a present for a friend or relative who likes cats? Look no further. *Alice's Diary*, the original memoirs of a very real six-year-old mixed tabby cat called Alice, explains precisely what it's like to be a cat. It's the nearest any of us will ever come to finding out exactly what cats think about themselves, other cats and us.

Until she started to keep this diary, Alice had hardly written anything. She certainly hadn't written anything for publication. But this, her first book, sparkles with wit and fun and a rare enthusiasm for life. She describes everything that happens to her and her half sister Thomasina with a keen eye for the absurd and a rare sense of wisdom.

Whether she is describing her relationship with the human beings with whom she shares her life (there are two of them – described as the Upright in Trousers and the Upright who wears a Skirt), her relationships with her many cat friends or her (not always successful) attempts at hunting, no cat lover will fail to find her story enchanting.

"Please send copies of *Alice's Diary* to the eleven friends on the accompanying list. It is a wonderful book which will give them all great pleasure." (MR R., LANCASHIRE)
"I felt I must put paw to paper to say how much my human and myself enjoyed your Diary." (THE W. FAMILY IN WEST SUSSEX)
"*Alice's Diary* is one of the nicest books I have ever read. She has wonderful insight." (MRS. J., LONDON)
"I am delighted with *Alice's Diary* – I must have *Alice's Adventures*." (V. H., GRIMSBY)
"One of the most delightful cat books in the world!" (MRS M.R., AUSTRALIA)

Over 60,000 delighted readers from around the world have already bought this beautifully-written and illustrated hardback book.

Our files are bursting with letters from confirmed fans (of all ages) who tell us how much they have enjoyed *Alice's Diary*.

Here is an extract from *Alice's Diary*

May 17th

Today I broke a vase. It was a complete accident. I jumped onto the mantelpiece and the vase just fell off. I don't think I touched it at all.

But the last time I broke a vase the Upright who wears a Skirt was furious. So this time I thought I'd stay out of the way for a while. Although it rained steadily all day I didn't go back into the house until it was absolutely pitch dark, and the Uprights had been calling me for several hours.

Sure enough, when I finally got back they were so pleased to see me that nothing at all was said about the vase.

Not that it was really my fault anyway.

ALICE'S ADVENTURES

£9.99 Hardback

After the publication of her hugely successful first book, Alice was inundated with fan mail urging her to put paw to paper once more. The result is this, her second volume of memoirs in which she shares with us yet another exciting and eventful year in her life.

Alice's Adventures is full of the wry, witty observations on life which so delighted the readers of her first book, and the wonderful illustrations capture the most poignant moments of her year.

ALICE AND OTHER FRIENDS

£12.99 Hardback

Thousands of readers have already discovered the joys of *Alice's Diary* and *Alice's Adventures* which have sold tens of thousands of copies and entranced animal lovers all over the world.

Vernon Coleman 'helped' Alice to write and illustrate these two books. Now, at last, here is Vernon Coleman's own account of life with Alice and her half sister Thomasina.

Charming, touching and intensely personal, this book is packed with stories, anecdotes and reminiscences about Alice and the many other creatures Vernon Coleman has met, known and lived with. There are, of course, many stories about Vernon Coleman's four pet sheep. The book is liberally and beautifully illustrated with numerous line drawings by the author.

THE CATS' OWN ANNUAL

£12.99 Hardback

Vernon claims (and we don't like to disagree with him about this) that there is a newspaper for cats called Cats' Own Paper, which is only available for cat subscribers. Vernon insists that to celebrate the newspaper's centenary he was been asked to compile an Annual so that 'Uprights' can see the world through a cat's eyes.

Here are just a few of the things you'll find inside this wonderful book…

- Reasons why cats are better than dogs
- Facts every cat-lover will want to know
- Best things about Uprights
- Worst things about Uprights
- Foods cats really like
- Foods cats really hate
- Quotes about cats
- Ways in which cats are superior to Uprights
- An ordinary day in the life of a cat
- The Cat Rules
- How you can extend your cat's lifespan by two or three years
- Problem pages for cats (and for Uprights)
- Poems and limericks

CATAHOLIC'S HANDBOOK

£12.99 Hardback

Full of wonderful illustrations, humour, anecdotes, poems and stories – which are so typical of all Vernon Coleman's cat books – all contained within a beautifully-bound hardback trademark yellow cover. Vernon Coleman's cat books truly are the crème de la crème of all cat books.

From proverbs to anecdotes, from curious facts to quizzes, *The Cataholic's Handbook* really does contain something for everyone who likes cats (and anyone who loves cats will love it all!).

Vernon Coleman's latest cat book, *The Cataholic's Handbook* is 182 pages long. And every page is just as exciting as the next.

Contents include:

- How well have you been trained by your cat?
- How intelligent is your cat? (Find out from this quiz if you are living with a furry genius!).
- Word games for cat lovers (a must for any lover of puzzles!).
- 'Pomes' about cats.
- How much have you learned from your cat?
- Thirty simple ways to make sure your cat loves you forever.
- The things people say about cats.
- A tour of Vernon Coleman's catland (you'll adore this!).
- A compilation of 229 strange and curious facts about cats (for example, why cats like being stroked; the sort of people cats prefer; what cats have to wear after dark if they live in Dallas, Texas, and much, much more).

THE CAT BASKET

£12.99 Hardback

Vernon Coleman's biggest ever cat book, decorated by the author with an ample collection of his trademark 'catoons'. If you've enjoyed any of Vernon Coleman's other cat books you will absolutely adore *The Cat Basket*. Britain's best-selling, best-loved cat book author has done it again!

Contents include:

- The telepathic link between cats and Uprights
- How to tell if you're a cataholic
- Three dozen assorted and amazing catfacts every cat lover should know
- So you thought you were potty about cats!
- Truly heroic cats: seven of the bravest cats of all time
- Why do cats climb trees?
- A dozen ways to keep your cat alive and healthy
- How much do you know about cats?
- Love letters to cats

CAT FABLES

£12.99 Hardback

We can learn a great deal from cats. I don't just mean that we can learn about their behaviour. We can also learn lessons that apply to us, too. Watch and listen to cats and we can learn an enormous amount that will help us through life.

How true are the stories in this book? Well, that's for you to decide. I'm not telling. And nor are the cats. But each story has been included because it contains a message; a 'moral' if you like. So these aren't so much stories as fables or parables.

Vernon Coleman

Contents Include:

- The Cat Who Found Out He Was Special
- The Man Who Hated Cats
- The Cat Magician
- The Fishing Expedition
- The Cat Who Had No Faith
- A Cat With Two Tails
- The Green Green Grass Of Home
- Calendar Girl
- The Gentle Art Of Sitting On A Lap
- No Time To Smell The Flowers
- The Sun Cat
- The Wisdom Of A Kitten
- The Cat Who Didn't Like Heights
- Princess Graceful And The Prince Of Charms
- The Good Listener
- The Big Mouse Hunt
- Climb The Impossible Dream
- The Price Of Everything And The Value Of Nothing
- The Feast
- The Cat With No Fear

- The Wisdom Of Fools
- The Legend
- Memories And Dreams
- The Worrier
- The Good Samaritan
- The Rebel
- Looking Down At Birds
- Badgers And Foxes And Dangerous Beasties
- The Big Bully
- Sunshine And Butterflies

"Containing 30 delightful stories about cats, each with a moral at the end, *Cat Fables* is another classic gem from writer Vernon Coleman. The book, with its trademark yellow cover, is illustrated with cat-toons"
YOUR CAT

WE LOVE CATS

£12.99 Hardback

If you love cats then you'll absolutely adore Vernon Coleman's book, *We Love Cats* – it's a real celebration of cats!

Following on in the tradition of Vernon Coleman's other cat books (*Alice's Diary* and *Alice's Adventures*) *We Love Cats* is packed with humour and insight into the way cats think, behave and quietly run our lives.

We Love Cats contains over 100 new and original squiggly Vernon Coleman drawings (he calls them 'catoons') plus loads of poems, limericks and amazing facts about cats.

We Love Cats will make a superb gift for any cat or animal lover. But, be warned: if you buy one you won't want to give it away!

In *We Love Cats* you will discover over 100 interesting and fascinating facts about cats and the truth about some popular cat myths.

THE SECRET LIVES OF CATS

£12.99 Hardback

This book takes the form of selected letters between two cats: Lemon-Coloured Lion Heart With Long Fine Whiskers and his mother (Maman), sent over a period of years. The cats did not actually write the letters, they communicated with each other by 'felipathy'. Dr Vernon Coleman is a trusted Upright (cat word for Human) with a proven track record of active support for animal rights and a deep love of cats, so he was chosen to edit and publish the letters in written form, thus enabling Uprights to have access to the wisdom, insights and adventures of Lemon and his mother, and other cats who touched their lives. It is illustrated throughout with Vernon Coleman's famous line drawings – catoons.

When Lemon is taken as a kitten to live with a new set of Uprights, he naturally misses his mother very much, and turns to her for support. She gently guides him in his task: "... to educate Uprights to lead them away from the path of indignant and false moral righteousness which some of their leaders have mistakenly chosen for them and to lead them back to a peaceful, loving coexistence."

Through his encounters with other cats and many different kinds of Upright, Lemon-Coloured Lion Heart matures from an enchantingly naive kitten to an adult cat with a dark, deep experience of life, love and tragedy.

"This beautiful and moving book, with its deadly serious underlying message, is in turn funny, sad, witty and entertaining. It is somewhat reminiscent of Anna Sewell's great Victorian classic *Black Beauty*, which did so much to further the cause of equine welfare. Let us hope that between them Lemon, Maman and Vernon Coleman can raise the consciousness of Uprights everywhere and do as much for cats as Anna Sewell did for horses." DEPARTED FRIEND

CAT TALES

£12.99 Hardback

This book is about people whose lives have been changed by cats.

Cats have always played a big part in my life. This collection of anecdotes, essays and memories describes some of the cats I have known, some of the ways in which they have affected my life and some of the ways in which they have affected the lives of others.

The stories in this book relate to incidents that happened to me, or that I observed myself. I have resisted the temptation to report stories which were told to me even if I heard them at first hand. When it comes to talking about cats some people can be inclined to exaggerate a little.

In particular I have resisted including stories which tell of cats who have learned tricks such as managing to open a door by jumping up and catching hold of the handle. Such feats are entirely feasible (I've witnessed them myself) but they are neither exceptional nor worthy of recording. And they certainly don't change the lives of the people who know the cats involved.

The one thing most of these tales have in common is that, in some way, someone's life was changed for the better, or was enriched, through knowing a cat. The effect cats can have on people can sometimes be slight and simple and sometimes subtle and complex. Unlike my book *Cat Fables*, there are, however, no lessons and no messages here. These stories are told simply for their own sake. I hope you enjoy them.

Vernon Coleman 2008

For a catalogue of Vernon Coleman's books
please write to:

Publishing House
Trinity Place
Barnstaple
Devon EX32 9HG
England

Telephone   01271 328892
Fax   01271 328768

Outside the UK:
Telephone   +44 1271 328892
Fax   +44 1271 328768

Or visit our website:
www.vernoncoleman.com